GRADE BY GRADE
TRUMPET

GRADE **1**

SELECTED BY
JANET WAY

BOOSEY&HAWKES

Janet Way

Janet Way is a tutor for the LRAM (Art of Teaching) woodwind course at the Royal Academy of Music. She was formerly a Mentor for the Associated Board of the Royal Schools of Music's Professional Development Course and an ABRSM Diploma examiner.

She studied with William Bennett, Geoffrey Gilbert and Marcel Moyse, and during her time at the Guildhall School of Music and Drama won a number of scholarships and prizes, including the prestigious Lord Mayor's Prize.

Janet has enjoyed a long career both as a performer and teacher, and for many years was a senior manager with the Oxfordshire Music Service. She is the director of the Oxford Flute Summer School which has an international reputation for excellence.

Published by Boosey & Hawkes Music Publishers Ltd
Aldwych House
71–91 Aldwych
London
WC2B 4HN

www.boosey.com

AN IMAGEM COMPANY

© Copyright 2013 by Boosey & Hawkes Music Publishers Ltd

ISMN 979-0-060-12484-6
ISBN 978-0-85162-719-9

Second impression 2017

Printed by Halstan:
Halstan UK, 2-10 Plantation Road, Amersham, Bucks, HP6 6HJ. United Kingdom
Halstan DE, Weißliliengasse 4, 55116 Mainz. Germany

Music origination by SEL Music Art Limited
Piano accompaniments, audio recording, mixing and mastering by Robin Bigwood
Trumpet performance by Heidi Bennett
Cover design by RF Design (UK) Limited

CONTENTS

FULL PERFORMANCE & BACKING TRACK CD

The enclosed CD contains demonstration and piano accompaniment backing tracks for all pieces as appropriate.

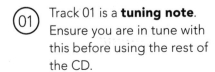 Track 01 is a **tuning note**. Ensure you are in tune with this before using the rest of the CD.

 Demonstration tracks are included for all pieces. Track numbers are shown in grey circles.

 Backing tracks are included for all accompanied pieces. Track numbers are shown in white circles.

THE BARLEY BREAK

Make sure the quavers are played with clean tonguing. This will give the melody a lively feel.

Traditional English
arr NICHOLAS HARE

DOUCEMENT À PETIT PAS

This piece can be played as a round, with each player or group beginning the piece at four-bar intervals.
Practise playing long notes at soft dynamics so you can start this piece *piano*.

ANON

UPSTAIRS, DOWNSTAIRS

There are five crotchet beats in each bar in this piece. Count carefully; no extra beats, please!
Lean on the dotted crotchet at the beginning of each bar to keep the music flowing.

ANTHONY MARKS

SCALE SPOT

The pieces on these pages are all in **C major**. There are no sharps or flats in this key signature.

Practise this scale now. Add a *crescendo* and *diminuendo* as you did in **Doucement à petit pas**.

Play the same scale in different rhythms and at contrasting dynamics.
The following step-wise pattern will prepare you well for the Japanese melody **Koinobori** (p4).

This pattern is in five. Clap the rhythm before you play.

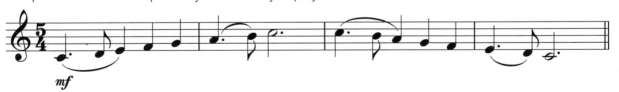

C major arpeggio is also a useful pattern with which to be familiar. Where is this used in **Sunrise** (p5)?

4

SIGHT-READING 1 ———————

Be a musical detective and look for the clues which tell you how this music will sound:

1. What is the time signature of this piece?
2. What does **Alla marcia** mean?
3. Find the crotchet rests and the minim rest.
4. Clap the rhythm of bar 6.

Set yourself a steady pulse and off you go!

JANET WAY

KOINOBORI

Why not try buzzing bar six on your mouthpiece before you play to help achieve a clean slur between the E and A?
What other notes can you slur to using this fingering?

Traditional Japanese

SUNRISE
from '100 easy studies for piano', op 139

Cantabile means 'in a singing style'. Breathe well so you can sustain the sound throughout the long phrases.

CARL CZERNY
arr NICHOLAS HARE

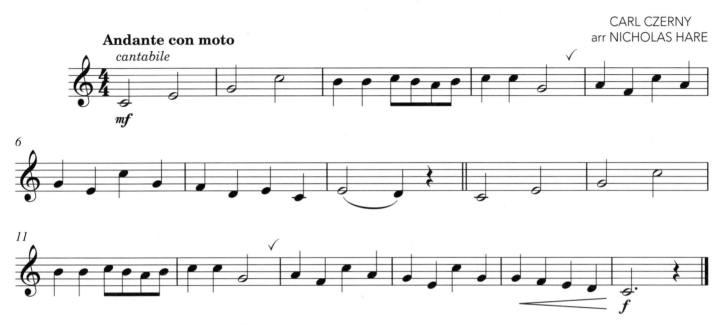

AURAL AWARENESS 1

For each of the following exercises, play the track or listen as your teacher plays the piano.

TASK A - FEEL THE PULSE (36)

As soon as you are able, join in with the music by clapping in time, placing an emphasis by way of a louder clap on the strong beats. Is the piece in two time or three time?

TASK B - ECHOES (37)

You will hear a key-chord and starting note, and then a series of two-bar phrases. Between each phrase there will be two bars of silence during which you should sing back the melody you have just heard. Make sure you don't leave a pause, and stay in time with the backing track.

TASK C - SPOT THE DIFFERENCE (38)

You will hear a key-chord and tonic, followed by a two-bar phrase. You will hear the phrase twice. Your task is to spot which note has been altered in terms of its pitch when played for the second time. Is it near the beginning or near the end?

TASK D - LISTENING (39)

Listen to the piece and then answer the following questions:
– How would you describe the dynamics in this piece? Was it loud or quiet?
– Did the dynamics change, and were these changes sudden or gradual?
– How would you describe the articulation in this piece? Was it played smoothly or detached?

METAL INSTRUMENT

Enjoy the heavy style of this piece. Make sure you count the rests carefully.

CHRISTOPHER NORTON

HUNGARIAN DANCE

Play with a light tonguing action and watch out for the $\frac{3}{4}$ bars, especially the rest at the end of bar 16.

EDWARD GREGSON

ONE HAND, ONE HEART
from 'West Side Story'

Imagine you are singing this tune as you play and be careful to count carefully during the dotted minims.

LEONARD BERNSTEIN
arr PETER LAWRANCE

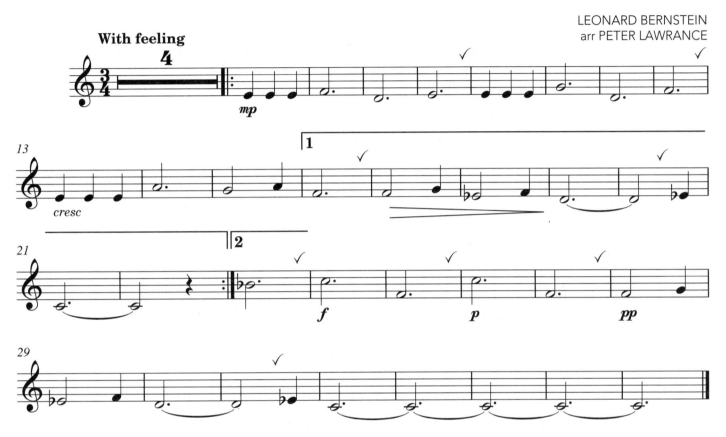

SIGHT-READING 2

Look for the clues about how this piece will sound:

1. What does **Allegretto** mean?
2. How will you play the last three notes?
3. Clap the rhythm all the way through and stamp in the rests.

Count two bars before you begin.

JANET WAY

GRANITE

Strong tonguing will help you achieve the solid rock style this piece demands. Keep the *staccato* passages crisp.
The first phrase is four bars long. How many times does it appear?

KEITH RAMON COLE

With a solid rock beat

MINUET

A minuet is a dance in three time. Always keep the third note (upbeat) *staccato*.
Aim to make a marked difference between the *f* and *p* passages.

JOSEPH HAYDN
arr CAROL BARRATT

Allegretto

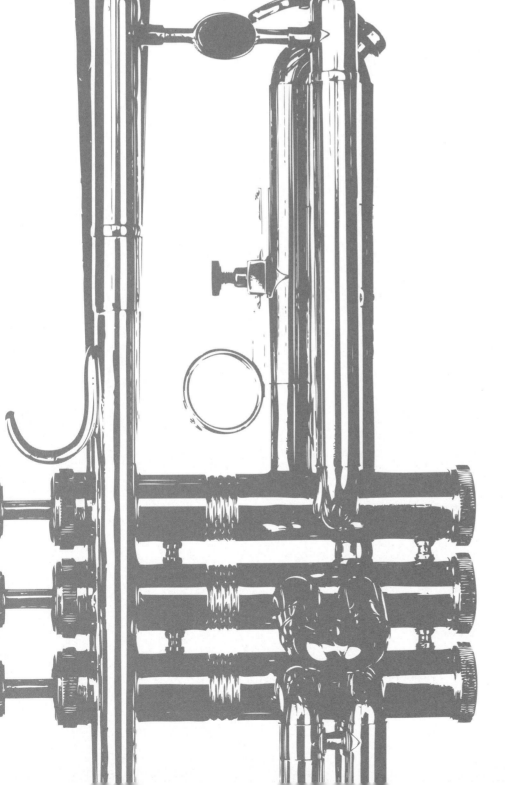

GRADE BY GRADE
TRUMPET

Piano Accompaniment

GRADE **1**

BOOSEY&HAWKES

Published by Boosey & Hawkes Music Publishers Ltd
Aldwych House
71–91 Aldwych
London
WC2B 4HN

www.boosey.com

© Copyright 2013 by Boosey & Hawkes Music Publishers Ltd

ISMN 979-0-060-12484-6
ISBN 978-0-85162-719-9

Second impression 2017

Printed by Halstan:
Halstan UK, 2-10 Plantation Road, Amersham, Bucks, HP6 6HJ. United Kingdom
Halstan DE, Weißliliengasse 4, 55116 Mainz. Germany

Music origination by SEL Music Art Limited
Piano accompaniments, audio recording, mixing and mastering by Robin Bigwood
Trumpet performance by Heidi Bennett
Cover design by RF Design (UK) Limited

CONTENTS

FULL PERFORMANCE & BACKING TRACK CD
The enclosed CD contains demonstration and piano accompaniment backing tracks for all pieces as appropriate.

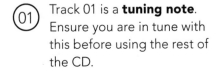 Track 01 is a **tuning note**. Ensure you are in tune with this before using the rest of the CD.

 Demonstration tracks are included for all pieces. Track numbers are shown in grey circles.

 Backing tracks are included for all accompanied pieces. Track numbers are shown in white circles.

THE BARLEY BREAK

Traditional English
arr NICHOLAS HARE

DOUCEMENT À PETIT PAS

Calm and gentle

ANON

KOINOBORI

Traditional Japanese

SUNRISE

from '100 easy studies for piano', op 139

CARL CZERNY
arr NICHOLAS HARE

METAL INSTRUMENT

CHRISTOPHER NORTON

ONE HAND, ONE HEART
from 'West Side Story'

LEONARD BERNSTEIN
arr PETER LAWRANCE

With feeling

GRANITE

KEITH RAMON COLE

MINUET

JOSEPH HAYDN
arr CAROL BARRATT

SHAKER MELODY

Traditional American

A WISTFUL WALTZ

MICHAEL JACQUES

Gently flowing

THE TRUMPET RAP

ANTHONY MARKS

FANFARONADE

CAROL BARRATT

TASK A - FEEL THE PULSE

Ask your student to join in with your piano playing by clapping in time as soon as they are able, placing an emphasis by way of a louder clap on the strong beats. Ask your student to identify whether the piece is in two time or three time.
Answer: This piece is in two time.

DMITRI KABALEVSKY

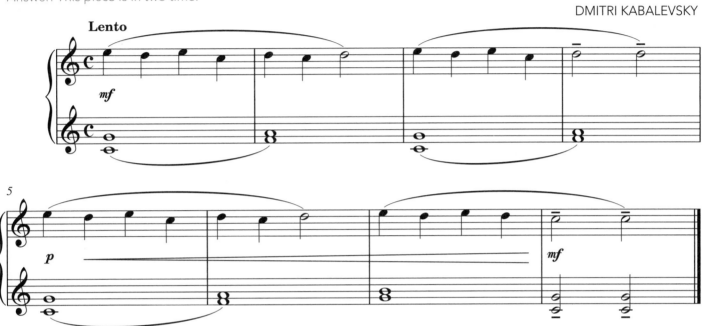

A little tune No 1 from 'Twenty-four little pieces' (op 39) © Copyright 1967 by Boosey & Hawkes Music Publishers Ltd

TASK B - ECHOES

Play the key-chord (C major) and starting note, then count in and play the series of two-bar phrases below. Your student should sing the melody they have just heard during the two bars of silence between each phrase. Ensure they don't leave a pause.

TASK C - SPOT THE DIFFERENCE

Play the the key-chord (C major) and tonic, then count in and play the two two-bar phrases below. Your student's task is to spot which note has been altered in terms of its pitch in the second phrase. Ask your student to identify whether the change is near the beginning or near the end. Answer: The pitch alteration occurs near the beginning.

TASK D - LISTENING

Play the piece used in Task A again and then ask your student the following questions:
– How would you describe the dynamics in this piece? Was it loud or quiet?
– Did the dynamics change, and were these changes sudden or gradual?
– How would you describe the articulation in this piece? Was it played smoothly or detached?

Answer: The piece started moderately loudly (*mezzo forte*), became suddenly quiet (*piano*) half-way through, then gradually increased in volume (*crescendo*) until the end. It was played smoothly (*legato*).

AURAL AWARENESS 2 (page 13)

TASK A - FEEL THE PULSE

Ask your student to join in with your piano playing by clapping in time as soon as they are able, placing an emphasis by way of a louder clap on the strong beats. Ask your student to identify whether the piece is in two time or three time. Answer: This piece is in two time.

DMITRI KABALEVSKY

Marching No 3 from 'Twenty-four little pieces' (op 39) © Copyright 1967 by Boosey & Hawkes Music Publishers Ltd

TASK B - ECHOES

Play the key-chord (F major) and starting note, then count in and play the series of two-bar phrases below. Your student should sing the melody they have just heard during the two bars of silence between each phrase. Ensure they don't leave a pause.

TASK C - SPOT THE DIFFERENCE

Play the the key-chord (F major) and tonic, then count in and play the two two-bar phrases below. Your student's task is to spot which note has been altered in terms of its pitch in the second phrase. Ask your student to identify whether the change is near the beginning or near the end. Answer: The pitch alteration occurs near the end.

TASK D - LISTENING

Play the piece used in Task A again and then ask your student the following questions:
– How would you describe the dynamics in this piece? Was it loud or quiet?
– Did the dynamics change, and were these changes sudden or gradual?
– How would you describe the articulation in this piece? Was it played smoothly or detached?
Answer: The piece was loud (*forte*) throughout. Most of the notes were detached from one another (*staccato*) although some, particularly at the ends of phrases, were held for their full length and given slightly more weight (*tenuto*).

AURAL AWARENESS 3 (page 16)

TASK A - FEEL THE PULSE

Ask your student to join in with your piano playing by clapping in time as soon as they are able, placing an emphasis by way of a louder clap on the strong beats. Ask your student to identify whether the piece is in two time or three time. Answer: This piece is in three time.

DMITRI KABALEVSKY

Extract from **A game** No 5 from 'Twenty-four little pieces' (op 39) © Copyright 1967 by Boosey & Hawkes Music Publishers Ltd

TASK B - ECHOES

Play the key-chord (B♭ major) and starting note, then count in and play the series of two-bar phrases below. Your student should sing the melody they have just heard during the two bars of silence between each phrase. Ensure they don't leave a pause.

TASK C - SPOT THE DIFFERENCE

Play the the key-chord (B♭ major) and tonic, then count in and play the two two-bar phrases below. Your student's task is to spot which note has been altered in terms of its pitch in the second phrase. Ask your student to identify whether the change is near the beginning or near the end. Answer: The pitch alteration occurs near the beginning.

TASK D - LISTENING

Play the piece used in Task A again and then ask your student the following questions:
– How would you describe the dynamics in this piece? Was it loud or quiet?
– Did the dynamics change, and were these changes sudden or gradual?
– How would you describe the articulation in this piece? Was it played smoothly or detached?
Answer: The piece started loudly (*forte*), but gradually became quieter (*diminuendo*) from the half-way point onwards, finally ending quietly (*piano*). It was played detached (*staccato*) with accents placed on the first beat of each bar.

NOTES

Also available from Boosey & Hawkes

LEARN AS YOU PLAY   FIRST REPERTOIRE PIECES   GRADE BY GRADE (GRADES 1-5)

CLARINET

FLUTE

OBOE

SAXOPHONE

TRUMPET

SHAKER MELODY

There are many arrangements of this beautiful tune. Make a real contrast between the *forte* and *piano* phrases.

Traditional American

COUNTRY DANCE

Be careful to play the slurs and to count the tied note for two beats in bars 14–15.

CLAUDE GERVAISE

A MINOR STUDY

Play with a full sound as you descend to the low As to ensure they are produced clearly.

FIONA BOLTON

SCALE SPOT

Both **A minor study** and **A wistful waltz** are in **A minor**.
This key is the relative minor of C major so there are no sharps or flats in its key signature.

A minor study uses a mixture of the harmonic minor scale and arpeggio patterns.

The G♮s used in **A wistful waltz** can be found in the melodic minor version of the scale.

What differences do you notice between the scales above and the A natural minor scale below?

A WISTFUL WALTZ

Try to feel the pulse of the waltz before you begin and count carefully in the $\frac{2}{4}$ bars. Listen out for the upbeat in the piano accompaniment at the end of bar 19 to ensure you move from the pause to the last note at the same time.

MICHAEL JACQUES

CREATIVE REFLECTION

Look at the shapes and play what you feel. Use any notes; there is no right or wrong way to play it!

JANET WAY

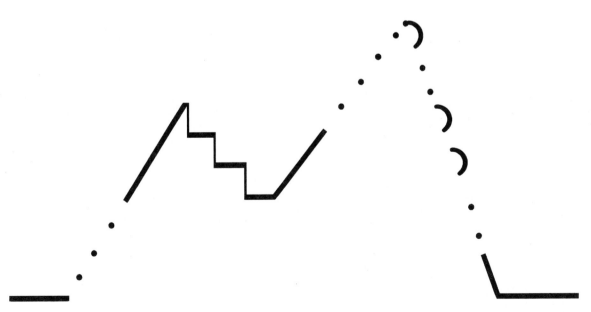

SIGHT-READING 3

Looking for the clues:

1. Is this piece in a major or a minor key?
2. What is the meaning of **Andante** and *legato*?
3. What is the mood of this piece?

Don't forget to set the pulse before you start.

JANET WAY

THE TRUMPET RAP

Listen to the piano accompaniment to get in the groove of this funky piece.

ANTHONY MARKS

TANGO

28

The dynamic contrasts and the crisp rhythms define the South American character of this dance.
Where do you go back to when you have played the last line?

CHRIS MORGAN

© Copyright 2004 by Boosey & Hawkes Music Publishers Ltd

AURAL AWARENESS 2

For each of the following exercises, play the track or listen as your teacher plays the piano.

TASK A - FEEL THE PULSE (40)

As soon as you are able, join in with the music by clapping in time, placing an emphasis by way of a louder clap on the strong beats. Is the piece in two time or three time?

TASK B - ECHOES (41)

You will hear a key-chord and starting note, and then a series of two-bar phrases. Between each phrase there will be two bars of silence during which you should sing back the melody you have just heard. Make sure you don't leave a pause, and stay in time with the backing track.

TASK C - SPOT THE DIFFERENCE (42)

You will hear a key-chord and tonic, followed by a two-bar phrase. You will hear the phrase twice. Your task is to spot which note has been altered in terms of its pitch when played for the second time. Is it near the beginning or near the end?

TASK D - LISTENING (43)

Listen to the piece and then answer the following questions:
– How would you describe the dynamics in this piece? Was it loud or quiet?
– Did the dynamics change, and were these changes sudden or gradual?
– How would you describe the articulation in this piece? Was it played smoothly or detached?

FANFARONADE

Here is a duet you can play with your teacher or a friend who plays another instrument in B♭ (clarinet, trombone etc).

Track 30 contains a demonstration of Part 1 with piano accompaniment.

Track 31 contains a demonstration of Part 2 with piano accompaniment.

Track 32 contains the piano accompaniment only.

The title of this piece means 'a flourish of trumpets'. Bring out the *staccato* notes to convey the energy of this duet.

CAROL BARRATT

CORUMBÁ

Here is another duet you can play with your teacher or a friend.
Track 34 contains a demonstration of Part 1 only.
Track 35 contains a demonstration of Part 2 only.

Have fun playing this lively duet and use the repeated quavers to capture the Brazilian feel.

PETER WASTALL

AURAL AWARENESS 3

For each of the following exercises, play the track or listen as your teacher plays the piano.

TASK A - FEEL THE PULSE

As soon as you are able, join in with the music by clapping in time, placing an emphasis by way of a louder clap on the strong beats. Is the piece in two time or three time?

TASK B - ECHOES

You will hear a key-chord and starting note, and then a series of two-bar phrases. Between each phrase there will be two bars of silence during which you should sing back the melody you have just heard. Make sure you don't leave a pause, and stay in time with the backing track.

TASK C - SPOT THE DIFFERENCE

You will hear a key-chord and tonic, followed by a two-bar phrase. You will hear the phrase twice. Your task is to spot which note has been altered in terms of its pitch when played for the second time. Is it near the beginning or near the end?

TASK D - LISTENING

Listen to the piece and then answer the following questions:
– How would you describe the dynamics in this piece? Was it loud or quiet?
– Did the dynamics change, and were these changes sudden or gradual?
– How would you describe the articulation in this piece? Was it played smoothly or detached?

NOTES

NOTES

Also available from Boosey & Hawkes

LEARN AS YOU PLAY   FIRST REPERTOIRE PIECES   GRADE BY GRADE (GRADES 1-5)

CLARINET

FLUTE

OBOE

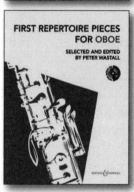

SAXOPHONE

TRUMPET

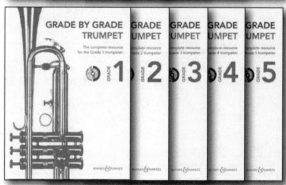